MICHAEL ROSE
THREE BIRTHDAY SONA[...]

THE ASSOCIATED BOARD OF
THE ROYAL SCHOOLS OF MUSIC

INTRODUCTION

Michael Rose studied the violin and piano at the Royal Academy of Music. After some years as a teacher, he became a Music Adviser and subsequently worked for the BBC Music Department in Bristol. In 1972 he returned to advisory work and is currently Music Inspector in Bedfordshire. Throughout his musical life he has conducted orchestras and choirs, and he composes in what little spare time remains.

These piano sonatinas, of about Grade 5 in standard, were written as birthday presents for his wife, a young friend and his daughter.

For Catherine

BIRTHDAY SONATINA No.1

MICHAEL ROSE

AB 2047

4

Andantino (♩. = 54)

calmato

8

simile

alla Coda ⊕

(l'istesso tempo)

legato espressivo, cantando

poco staccato (come pizz.)

simile

simile

mp

mf legato molto

For Anna

BIRTHDAY SONATINA No. 2

MICHAEL ROSE

Allegro giocoso ($\bullet$ = 120/126)

For Nansi

BIRTHDAY SONATINA No. 3

MICHAEL ROSE

AB 2047

Reproduced and printed by
Halstan & Co. Ltd., Amersham, Bucks., England